Michigan Snakes

SO-BJM-353

A Field Guide and Pocket Reference

by

J. Alan Holman and James H. Harding
MSU Department of Zoology

The authors acknowledge contributions of
Marvin M. Hensley, MSU Department of Zoology (dec.), and
Glenn R. Dudderar, MSU Department of Fisheries and Wildlife (ret.)

Photography *(except as noted)*:
James H. Harding

Editorial Assistance:
Technical Advisory Committee on Amphibians and Reptiles — MDNR
Robert Hess, DNR Non-Game Wildlife Fund Natural Heritage Program

Layout, Editing and Project Management:
Alicia Burnell, Leslie Johnson and Ken Fettig
ANR Communications, Michigan State University

Cover photos:
(front) Western Fox Snake; *(back)* Smooth Green Snake

ISBN 1-56525-020-6

© 2006, Michigan State University
Revised Edition, 2006

Introduction

Of all living reptiles, snakes undoubtedly elicit the strongest emotions in people. Though many people fear snakes, the number of people who are fascinated by these animals and appreciate their importance in the environment is growing every year. Knowledge and familiarity can turn fear into respect, and we hope that this book will further this goal.

This book is a guide to the identification of the 18 native species of snakes found in Michigan. It also includes information on the general biology of snakes, snake conservation and relations with people (including snake problems around the home and snakebite). This book is intended for use by the general public and should also prove useful to local and state resource managers. It is not, however, intended as a technical reference for professional herpetologists.

Snakes, and their close relatives the lizards, are reptiles, an animal group that also includes the turtles, crocodilians and (technically) the birds. Snakes have an internal bony skeleton, breathe air with lungs, get their body warmth from their surroundings and hibernate in the winter (if they live where winter temperatures are below freezing for long periods). Living snakes do not have legs, external ear openings or movable eyelids. They do have a transparent, immovable eye covering; a dry, scaly outer skin that is shed in one piece; and a skull with movable bones and loosely connected jaws that can spread widely so snakes can swallow food whole.

To identify a snake in Michigan, compare it with the photographs in this book. If you find a picture that looks like the snake, look at the range map to see if that species is known to occur in the area where the snake was observed. If so, then carefully read the "Identification" section to confirm your ID. Be careful — at first glance, different snake species may look quite similar, but you can distinguish one from another by looking at details of color, shape and size. Note that the size range given for each species is the total (head to tail) length for mature (adult) individuals.

The "Habitat and Habits" section will also help in snake identification. For example, a thick-bodied snake with an upturned "nose" ("Identification" section) found in a sandy woodland eating a toad ("Habitat and Habits" section) near Lake Michigan (range map) can be positively identified as an Eastern Hog-nosed Snake, even without the aid of a picture.

If you can closely examine a snake, another way to identify it is to use the "Simplified Key to Michigan Snakes" (beginning on page 8). To use the key, start at the first set of paired descriptions and choose the statement ("a" or "b") that better fits your snake and proceed to the next number indicated and compare those two statements. Again, pick the better fit and proceed as indicated and so on. By this process of elimination, you will eventually arrive at the name of the snake and the page number of its picture and description. Then read the species account and check the range map to verify your identification. The illustrations on page 6 show the identifying characteristics used in the key.

Most snake species have a rather uneven distribution in Michigan because of limited habitat availability, differences in temperature tolerances, and the effects of human modifications of the environment.

Thus, the range maps are only a general representation of each species' distribution in Michigan. The most common snake in Michigan, the Eastern Gartersnake, has been recorded from every county in the state and occurs in a wide variety of habitats. All of our other species are, by comparison, more restricted in range and/or habitat preferences, though some can be locally common where conditions are suitable.

Note: New methods of studying the relationships of snakes, including the use of DNA analysis, can result in changes in the classification and naming of snake species. Differing interpretations of published studies can sometimes lead to (usually temporary) disagreement among snake experts over which names are preferable. In this book, we largely follow the latest available checklist and addenda published by the Committee on Common and Scientific Names, Society for the Study of Amphibians and Reptiles (Crother et al., 2000) with further guidance from the text by Ernst and Ernst (2003). Some names used here differ from those used in the first edition of this book, and additional changes can be expected as our knowledge increases.

Checklist for Michigan Snakes

P ut a checkmark by the name of each species when you observe and successfully identify it in the wild in Michigan. You may also want to note the date of observation and the location.

Page numbers are the first page of each species' account.

Family Colubridae

Subfamily Natricinae

Subfamily Xenodontinae

Subfamily Colubrinae

Family Viperidae

Subfamily Crotalinae

Identifying Characteristics of Michigan Snakes

Use these illustrations with the key on page 8 to help you identify any snake found in Michigan.

Figure 1

Figure 2

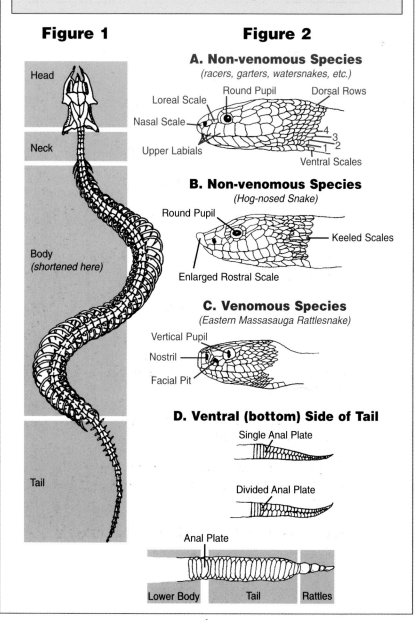

Head

Neck

Body
(shortened here)

Tail

A. Non-venomous Species
(racers, garters, watersnakes, etc.)

Loreal Scale
Nasal Scale
Upper Labials
Round Pupil
Dorsal Rows
4
3
2
1
Ventral Scales

B. Non-venomous Species
(Hog-nosed Snake)

Round Pupil
Keeled Scales
Enlarged Rostral Scale

C. Venomous Species
(Eastern Massasauga Rattlesnake)

Vertical Pupil
Nostril
Facial Pit

D. Ventral (bottom) Side of Tail

Single Anal Plate

Divided Anal Plate

Anal Plate

Lower Body
Tail
Rattles

Figure numbers refer to illustrations on page 6.

anal plate — scale above anal opening *(Fig. 2d)*

band — a patch of color running across the back of a snake (side to side)

blotch — an irregular patch of color

dorsal — back or top side of a snake

keel — small ridge along the center of the scales in some species *(Fig. 2b)*

labial scales — scales bordering a snake's mouth *(Fig. 2a)*

loreal scale — scale between the eye and the nostril *(Fig. 2a)*

pit — paired heat-sensing organs on the head of a rattlesnake, between eye and nostril *(Fig. 2c)*

rostral scale — scale on the front tip of a snake's head *(Fig. 2b)*

stripe — a narrow strip of color running along the length of the back or sides of a snake

ventral — the belly or underside of a snake *(Fig. 2a & 2d)*

A Simplified Key to Michigan Snakes

To use this key, start at the first set of paired descriptions and compare the two sets of characteristics given. Choose the one (a or b) that better fits the snake and proceed to the next number indicated and compare those two. By this process of elimination, you will eventually arrive at the name of the snake and the page number of its picture, range map and description. The illustrations on page 6 and the definitions on page 7 will help you use this key.

1. (a) A pit between eye and nostril *(Fig. 2c)*; tail ending in a rattle...
   Sistrurus catenatus catenatus, Eastern Massasauga
   See page 54

   (b) No pit between eye and nostril; tail pointed
   Go to number 2

2. (a) Keels on some or all of dorsal scales of body and tail *(Fig. 2b)*
   Go to number 3

   (b) Dorsal scales smooth *(Fig. 2a)*
   Go to number 16

3. (a) Anal plate divided *(Fig. 2d)*
   Go to number 4

   (b) Anal plate single *(Fig. 2d)*
   Go to number 14

4. (a) Rostral scale turned up and keeled above *(Fig. 2b)*
   Heterodon platirhinos, Eastern Hog-nosed Snake
   See page 36

   (b) Rostral scale normal *(Fig. 2a)*
   Go to number 5

5. (a) No loreal, size small (12 inches or less)
   Go to number 6

(b) Loreal present *(Fig. 2a)*, adults usually larger than 12 inches
Go to number 8

6. (a) Scale rows 17 in number *(Fig. 2a)*; belly buff to light brown or pinkish
Go to number 7

(b) Scale rows 15; belly red....
Storeria occipitomaculata occipitomaculata, Northern Red-bellied Snake
See page 24

7. (a & b) Dorsal spots separate or fused to form crossbars; dark spot may or may not be present under eye...
Storeria dekayi (subspecies), Brownsnake
— see text for explanation
See page 22

8. (a) Dorsal scales weakly keeled (keels barely visible)
Go to number 9

(b) Dorsal scales strongly keeled (keels easily seen) *(Fig. 2b)*
Go to number 11

9. (a) Adult black above or with obscure blotches; juveniles spotted; 25 to 27 scale rows...
Pantherophis spiloides, Central Ratsnake
See page 42

(b) Adults and juveniles yellowish to brown above with dark blotches; 23 to 25 scale rows
Go to number 10

10. (a) 33 to 51 dorsal blotches (average 41); anterior dorsal blotches usually 3 or 4 scales in length (Upper Peninsula)...
Pantherophis vulpinus, Western Foxsnake
See page 46

(b) 20 to 43 dorsal blotches (average 34); anterior dorsal blotches usually more than 4 scales in length (eastern Lower Peninsula)...
Pantherophis gloydi, Eastern Foxsnake
See page 46

11. (a) Scale rows 17 to 19 in number
Go to number 12

(b) Scale rows 21 or more in number
Go to number 13

12. (a) A yellow stripe on side and 3 black lines on back; belly yellow with 4 dark stripes...
Regina septemvittata, Queen Snake
See page 20

(b) Back reddish brown with 4 rows of round black spots; belly reddish, with a row of black spots on either side...
Clonophis kirtlandii, Kirtland's Snake
See page 12

13. (a) Back uniformly black or brown, sometimes with faint dorsal blotches; belly uniformly red, orange or pink...
Nerodia erythrogaster neglecta, Copper-bellied Watersnake
See page 14

(b) Back brown with dorsal blotches often uniting with lateral spots to form cross bands; belly mottled or with crescent-shaped spots...
Nerodia sipedon sipedon, Northern Watersnake
See page 16

14. (a) Tail at least one-third of total length; lateral yellow stripe on scale rows 3 and 4 above the ventrals...
Thamnophis sauritus septentrionalis, Northern Ribbonsnake
See page 32

(b) Tail length less than one-third of total length
Go to number 15

15. (a) Upper labials normally 7; lateral yellow stripe on scale rows 2 and 3...
Thamnophis sirtalis sirtalis, Eastern Gartersnake
See page 26

(b) Upper labials normally 6; lateral yellow stripe involves scale rows 2, 3 and 4; head about same width as neck...
Thamnophis butleri, Butler's Gartersnake
See page 30

16. (a) Anal plate single; black-bordered brown blotches on back; top of head with a Y-shaped light spot; belly with a checkerboard pattern...
Lampropeltis triangulum triangulum, Eastern Milksnake
See page 50

(b) Anal plate divided
Go to number 17

17. (a) Nasal scale single with nostril in center *(Fig. 2a)*; body color uniform green....
Opheodrys vernalis, Smooth Greensnake
See page 52

(b) Two nasal scales with nostril between them *(Fig. 2b)*; body not green
Go to number 18

18. (a) A yellow ring around neck; uniformly blackish above; belly yellowish...
Diadophis punctatus edwardsii, Northern Ring-necked Snake
See page 34

(b) No light collar; adults uniformly bluish to black above with a white chin; belly lighter blue; large size...
Coluber constrictor foxii, Blue Racer
See page 40

KIRTLAND'S SNAKE

Juvenile

KIRTLAND'S SNAKE
(Clonophis kirtlandii)

Identification:

The Kirtland's Snake is a small (12 to 24 inches), reddish brown snake with black, often indistinct blotches in four rows down its back and a black head. The belly is brick-red with a row of black spots down each side. When disturbed, this snake will often flatten its body to a remarkable degree and may then remain motionless unless touched.

It may be confused with the Northern Red-bellied Snake (page 25), but the Red-bellied Snake lacks black spots along the belly and has no blotches on its back.

Distribution:

Kirtland's Snake is an extremely rare species in Michigan. It has been found in a very few localities in the southern one-third of the Lower Peninsula. Most of the specimens found in Michigan have been reported from the two southernmost tiers of counties.

Habitat and Habits:

This rarely seen snake occurs in a variety of moist habitats, which include wet meadows, tamarack swamps, open swamp-forest and vacant city lots. Earthworms and slugs are the favorite foods of Kirtland's Snake. This secretive species is believed to spend most of its time underground in the burrows of crayfish and other small animals. The tiny 5- to 6-inch young are born in late summer. There are usually five to 15 in a litter.

Kirtland's Snake is listed as ENDANGERED by the Michigan Department of Natural Resources (DNR) and is protected in the state. It is illegal to possess or handle this snake. Any sightings of this species should be reported to the DNR Wildlife Division, Lansing, Michigan.

COPPER-BELLIED WATERSNAKE

R.W. VanDevender

Juvenile

COPPER-BELLIED WATERSNAKE

(Nerodia erythrogaster neglecta)

Identification:

The Copper-bellied Watersnake is a medium-sized to large (30 to 56 inches) snake, uniformly colored dark brown or black. The belly is reddish, orange or yellow, and it may be shaded at the edges by the darker color of the back. Young individuals are brownish with a blotched dorsal pattern; the blotches may remain visible in some adult specimens.

The Northern Watersnake (page 16), which may occur in the same habitat, usually retains a blotched or banded pattern into adulthood and has half-moon-shaped dark spots on the belly (page 19).

Distribution:

The Copper-bellied Watersnake is extremely rare in Michigan and is now found in only a few locations in the southern one-third of the Lower Peninsula. Most recent records are in Hillsdale and St. Joseph counties.

Habitat and Habits:

Copper-bellied Watersnakes are usually found near streams, woodland ponds and river-bottom swamps. They apparently avoid fast-moving waters. Most often seen sunning on logs, banks or piles of debris at the water's edge, this species may occasionally wander away from water. They feed on amphibians (frogs, tadpoles) and small fish. The young are born in litters of five to 37, usually in late summer or fall.

The Copper-bellied Watersnake is listed as ENDANGERED by the Michigan Department of Natural Resources (DNR) and is protected by state and federal law. It is illegal to possess or handle this snake. Any sightings of this species should be reported to the DNR Wildlife Division, Lansing, Michigan.

Juvenile

NORTHERN WATERSNAKE
(Nerodia sipedon sipedon)

Identification:

A medium to large (24 to 55 inches), dark-colored snake seen in or near water is likely to be this species. Most specimens have dark brown or blackish blotches or bands on a lighter brown background, but older individuals may appear uniformly black.

Unlike the rare Copper-bellied Watersnake (page 14) with its plain reddish underside, the Northern Watersnake usually has red, orange or black spots, usually half-moon-shaped, on both sides of the belly. The strongly keeled scales of these water snakes give them a dull appearance.

The young (page 16) are more distinctly patterned than adults, with dark bands on a light gray background.

Distribution:

Northern Watersnakes occur throughout Michigan but are scarce or absent from many parts of the Upper Peninsula, particularly the western section. Some islands, such as Beaver Island in northern Lake Michigan, support large populations.

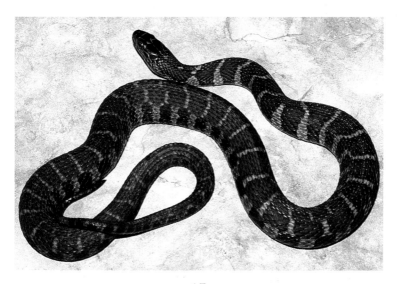

Habitat and Habits:

This species is usually found in or near ponds, lakes, streams or rivers. They are often seen sunning alongside the water on logs, overhanging branches, rockpiles and old bridge abutments. When disturbed, they glide rapidly into the water and can swim well, both on the surface and submerged. Water snakes are harmless but are frequently misidentified as "water moccasins" and assumed to be venomous. This has led to needless persecution, and many areas that once had large populations of Northern Watersnakes now have few or none.

Watersnakes are nervous and usually try to bite if cornered or restrained. If handled, they release a foul-smelling anal secretion.

Northern Watersnakes feed on frogs and fish and are frequently seen eating dead fish. They are often falsely accused of harming game fish populations, but they may actually benefit sport fishing by consuming stunted, overcrowded fish.

Female Northern Watersnakes give birth to four to 50 or more young in late summer or fall.

Belly

Juvenile

R.W. VanDevender

Juvenile

QUEEN SNAKE
(Regina septemvittata)

Identification:

The Queen Snake is a small to medium-sized (12 to 36 inches), slender, dark brown to gray-brown snake with a conspicuous, light stripe along each side of the body. In some specimens, three narrow, dark stripes may be visible running down the back. The belly is yellowish or whitish with four dark brown stripes; the two outer stripes are wider than the inner pair. In adults, the belly stripes may obscure the light color on the lower belly area. Queen Snakes sometimes are confused with Ribbon- and Gartersnakes (pages 26-33), but these lack the dark belly stripes and usually have a light stripe down the middle of the back. Young Queen Snakes are similar to adults, but their markings are more distinct.

Distribution:

The Queen Snake is uncommon to rare and occurs in scattered locations throughout the southern half of the Lower Peninsula, excluding portions of the Thumb area. Isolated occurrences are known in Ogemaw County and on Bois Blanc Island in northern Lake Huron.

Habitat and Habits:

The Queen Snake is most often seen basking in the branches of shrubs that overhang shallow, rocky streams, but it also frequents the edges of ponds or canals. When disturbed, it drops into the water and swims to the bottom, hiding under submerged objects. The Queen Snake may bite and will release a foul-smelling musk when handled.

Queen Snakes usually eat crayfish, especially those that have recently molted and are still soft. The young are born in late summer in litters numbering from five to 31.

BROWNSNAKE

Juvenile

BROWNSNAKE
(Storeria dekayi)

Identification:

The Brownsnake is a very small (9 to 18 inches) brown or gray-brown snake, usually with two rows of parallel dark dots down the back that border a lighter middle stripe. These dots sometimes join to form bars across the back. It has a dark, downward-oriented streak on each side of its head. The pale yellowish, brownish or pinkish belly may be edged with small black spots. The tiny newborn young are usually black, with a pale yellowish spot or band on the neck.

Distribution:

Brownsnakes occur throughout Michigan's Lower Peninsula but are uncommon and local in the Upper Peninsula. The Brownsnake population in the Lower Peninsula is intermediate between the Northern Brownsnake (*Storeria d. dekayi*) and the Midland Brownsnake (*S. d. wrightorum*). Those in the Upper Peninsula are intergrades between the Texas Brownsnake (*S. d. texana*) and the Midland race. This mixing of subspecies may account for the variation in color pattern seen in Michigan Brownsnakes.

Habitat and Habits:

The Brownsnake is secretive and is usually found in moist locations hiding under flat objects. They are often found in vacant city lots and disturbed areas.

Brownsnakes are most active in the spring and fall or after heavy rain showers, when they may be seen crawling across roads and sidewalks. These gentle creatures rarely bite, even when provoked. This species usually eats worms and slugs.

Females give birth to litters of five to 30 or more young in mid- to late summer.

NORTHERN
RED-BELLIED SNAKE

Juvenile

NORTHERN RED-BELLIED SNAKE
(Storeria occipitomaculata occipitomaculata)

Identification:

The Northern Red-bellied Snake is very small, usually less than 12 inches long, with a back color of brown, reddish brown or gray, sometimes with faint lengthwise stripes down the back. The belly is red, pink or orangish, without the double row of black spots seen in Kirtland's Snake (page 12).

The head is very small, and most individuals have three whitish spots behind the head that often fuse to form a light collar on the neck. This collar is less distinct than that of the Northern Ring-necked Snake (page 34). In the Upper Peninsula, this snake is commonly called the "copper-belly." The tiny newborn young are black with a light spot behind the head.

Distribution:

This snake is found statewide except for the extreme southern edge of the Lower Peninsula. Although it may be rare or absent in many areas within its range, this snake can be locally abundant in some places.

Habitat and Habits:

The Northern Red-bellied Snake can be found in a variety of habitats, including open woodland, meadows and abandoned farmland. It is often found under boards and debris in old dumps and trash piles.

This gentle snake is not known to bite but may curl up its "lips" when frightened or threatened. Earthworms and slugs are the favored foods. Females give birth to litters of one to 21 young in mid- to late summer.

EASTERN GARTERSNAKE

Juvenile

EASTERN GARTERSNAKE
(Thamnophis sirtalis sirtalis)

Identification:

The three kinds of gartersnakes in Michigan — Eastern, Butler's and Northern Ribbon — are small to moderate-sized, with three characteristic lengthwise stripes — one on each side and one down the middle of the back. They differ in body proportions and position of the side stripes. If you count the scale rows from the large belly scales to the center of the back, you will notice that the side stripes cover different rows in each species. In the Eastern Gartersnake, this stripe is confined to scale rows 2 and 3. The stripe occurs on rows 2, 3 and 4 in Butler's Gartersnake (page 30), and on rows 3 and 4 in the Northern Ribbonsnake (page 32).

The Eastern Gartersnake is a medium-sized to large (18 to 54 inches) snake with an extremely variable color pattern. The background color may be black, brown or olive-green, and the three yellow, white or greenish stripes may be sharply delineated or dull and obscured.

Many individuals have dark spots between the stripes, often giving the animals a checkered appearance. Some individuals have a reddish orange coloring between the stripes. The belly is pale yellow, greenish or blue. The young are similar to the adults.

Distribution:

The Eastern Gartersnake is probably the most common Michigan snake and occurs throughout the state.

Habitat and Habits:

Woodlands, meadows, marshes, lake edges, debris piles and suburban backyards are all homes for this tolerant species. The Eastern Gartersnake shows a preference for damp places that support its favorite foods — earthworms, frogs, toads and small fish. In urbanized areas, gartersnakes seem able to live on a diet of worms.

This species varies greatly in temperament. Some specimens flatten their bodies and attempt to bite when approached, while others make no attempt to bite, even when frightened or threatened. Nearly all will smear an unpleasant anal secretion on a restraining hand. They are alert, active animals but are not as nervous as their close relative, the Northern Ribbonsnake (page 32).

Mating occurs soon after emergence from hibernation in early spring. Baby Eastern Gartersnakes are born in litters of six to more than 50 during midsummer.

Eating American Toad.

Juvenile

Juvenile

BUTLER'S GARTERSNAKE
(Thamnophis butleri)

Identification:

Butler's Gartersnake is a small to medium-sized (15 to 29 inches), stout-bodied, striped snake with a small, dark head. The lateral light-colored stripes on the forward part of the body are on scale row 3 and the adjacent halves of rows 2 and 4.

The background color is black, brown or olive, and the stripes are yellow and quite distinct. Some specimens display dark spots between the dorsal and side stripes.

When excited, this snake often wiggles violently back and forth with little forward movement. Compare with the Eastern Gartersnake (page 26) and the Northern Ribbonsnake (page 32).

Distribution:

Butler's Gartersnake occurs in scattered populations in the eastern and south central Lower Peninsula of Michigan.

Habitat and Habits:

This snake prefers moist meadows, marshes and the grassy edges of lakes and streams. Large populations may occur in vacant urban lots.

Butler's Gartersnake is gentle and rarely attempts to bite but will release an unpleasant musky secretion when handled. Earthworms are the favored food, but small amphibians are sometimes eaten. This species becomes tame in captivity and can live for some time on a diet of worms.

Females give birth in midsummer to litters of four to 20 young, which are miniatures of the adult.

NORTHERN RIBBONSNAKE
(Thamnophis sauritus septentrionalis)

Identification:

The Northern Ribbonsnake is 18 to 34 inches long, slender and striped, with a long tail that is about one-quarter to one-third the total length of the snake. Bright yellow or white stripes are distinct against the brown or black background color. The side stripes are on scale rows 3 and 4.

The head is long and narrow with bright, unmarked, whitish labial scales along the edge of the mouth.

Both the Eastern Gartersnake (page 26) and Butler's Garter Snake (page 30) have stouter bodies and shorter tails in relation to total length than the Northern Ribbonsnake.

Distribution:

The Northern Ribbonsnake occurs throughout Michigan's Lower Peninsula.

Habitat and Habits:

This species inhabits the grassy edges of marshes, ponds, lakes and streams. They swim well but rarely dive underwater. Ribbon snakes are alert, active animals, and when disturbed they can glide through dense vegetation with surprising speed. Frogs, tadpoles, salamanders and small fish are the favored foods. Unlike other garter snakes, ribbon snakes normally do not eat earthworms.

Northern Ribbonsnakes rarely bite when handled but will smear a captor with a rather sweetish smelling musk. Females will give birth to three to 20 or more young in July or August.

NORTHERN
RING-NECKED SNAKE

Juvenile

NORTHERN RING-NECKED SNAKE
(Diadophis punctatus edwardsii)

Identification:

The Northern Ring-necked Snake is a small (10 to 20 + inches), shiny, slate-gray to bluish black snake with a yellow ring around its neck. The body scales are very smooth; the belly is plain light yellow, occasionally with a few dark spots along the midline. The young are darker than the adults but otherwise similar.

Distribution:

Although the Northern Ring-necked Snake has been found throughout Michigan, it is generally rare and occurs in widely scattered and isolated populations. It appears to be most common in the north, particularly near the northen Lake Michigan coast and on some of the larger offshore islands.

Habitat and Habits:

This species prefers moist woodlands. It is very secretive and is usually found hiding under flat objects or the bark of dead trees. Northern Ring-necked Snakes are inoffensive and rarely bite when handled. They feed on earthworms, amphibians and, occasionally, other snakes. In Michigan, they are reported to feed largely on the Red-backed Salamander (Plethodon cinereus).

Female Northern Ring-necked Snakes lay from one to 10 elongated eggs in rotted wood or under loose bark, usually in late June. Hatching occurs in late summer.

EASTERN HOG-NOSED SNAKE

EASTERN HOG-NOSED SNAKE
(Heterodon platirhinos)

Identification:

The Eastern Hog-nosed Snake is a stout-bodied snake 20 to 45 inches long, with an upturned snout. It is highly variable in color; most have dark spots and blotches on a yellowish, reddish or brown background, but some are solid black, brown or olive.

When encountered in the field, this harmless snake will often spread its neck, somewhat like a cobra, and hiss loudly. This defensive behavior has resulted in people giving this snake a number of evil-sounding nicknames, such as "puff adder" or "spreading viper."

Distribution:

Although it occurs over much of Michigan's Lower Peninsula, in the Upper Peninsula the Eastern Hog-nosed Snake has been found only in Menominee County.

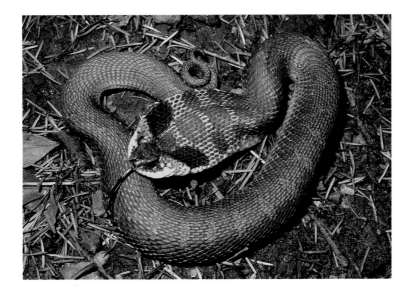

Habitat and Habits:

The Eastern Hog-nosed Snake is usually found in sandy areas, especially in the open, sandy woods of the northern and western Lower Peninsula. It uses its upturned snout to dig for toads, its favorite food. It also occasionally eats frogs, salamanders and young rodents.

The defensive display of this snake is remarkable. When disturbed, the Hog-nosed Snake will flatten out its neck, coil its body and its tail, and hiss loudly. It may strike out repeatedly at a threatening object, but nearly always with its mouth closed. Each strike is also accompanied by a sharp hiss.

This bluffing display presumably deters natural enemies such as skunks, foxes and raccoons. Many people will either flee or, unfortunately, grab a rock or stick and kill the bluffing snake, and thus miss the next part of the Hog-nosed Snake's defensive routine. If a bluffing snake is teased or grabbed, it may suddenly seem to become violently ill, appear to go into convulsions with mouth agape and tongue dragging in the dirt, and smear feces over its body. Then it will turn onto its back, lie perfectly still and appear to be dead. Amazingly, if the "dead" snake is put "right side up" by the observer, it quickly turns on its back again, as if a dead snake must be "belly-up"! If the supposed enemy leaves, the snake soon lifts its head, tests the air with its tongue, and then crawls away as fast as possible.

There is much variation between Hognosed Snakes in how much of this bluffing routine is used in a given situation; some individuals may skip portions of the routine or simply try to escape.

Female Eastern Hog-nosed Snakes lay from four to more than 50 eggs underground in early summer. These hatch 60 to 70 days later into 6- to 10-inch snakes that are capable of hissing and neck-spreading before they are even free of their eggshells.

Juvenile

"Playing dead"

39

BLUE RACER

Juvenile

BLUE RACER
(Coluber constrictor foxii)

Identification:

The Blue Racer is a large (4 to 6 feet), active snake with a solid bluish, greenish or gray back and a lighter, bluish belly. The head is darker than the body, and the throat and chin are white. These snakes are smooth-scaled and shiny. Newly hatched and young Blue Racers have a pattern of reddish brown or gray blotches and spots on a gray background (see photo, page 40). This pattern fades as the snakes mature and is usually gone by the time they reach 3 feet in length.

Distribution:

This species occurs in the southern and western counties of Michigan's Lower Peninsula. Though their numbers appear to be declining in the south, Blue Racers may be becoming more widespread in the northwestern Lower Peninsula. Records also exist for Menominee County in the Upper Peninsula.

Habitat and Habits:

Blue Racers live in a variety of habitats, such as open woods, meadows, abandoned farmlands, raspberry thickets, and the edges of lakes and marshes.

They are alert, active snakes that gracefully glide away when approached, often climbing into low shrubs or trees to escape. When cornered, racers will coil and strike, and their tiny, sharp teeth can cause minor cuts on a human hand, but they are not venomous.

Racers eat rodents, frogs, other snakes, birds and insects. Despite the scientific name "constrictor," racers do not constrict prey, but they may press larger food items against the ground with a loop of the body before and during swallowing.

Females lay from six to 32 eggs in rotted wood, humus or moist sand during June or July. The young snakes hatch in late summer.

CENTRAL (BLACK) RATSNAKE

Egg and hatchling

CENTRAL (BLACK) RATSNAKE
(Pantherophis spiloides)

Identification:

The Central Ratsnake is a large, shiny, dark gray to black snake with a white chin and throat. This is Michigan's largest snake. Adults often exceed 6 feet in length; the record is over 8 feet. Hatchlings and juveniles are strongly patterned with dark blotches on a lighter gray background. Traces of this juvenile pattern are often visible in adult ratsnakes, though it may be reduced to a few scattered flecks of white or gray between the scales.

Distribution:

In Michigan the Central Ratsnake is an uncommon to rare and localized species restricted to the southern half of the Lower Peninsula; it's most often observed in the southwestern counties. **This snake is listed as a "Species of Special Concern" by the Michigan Department of Natural Resources, and it may not be captured or killed.**

Habitat and Habits:

Central Ratsnakes usually inhabit woodlands and woodland edges but are occasionally found in and around barns and outbuildings. They are quite arboreal and often forage and bask at considerable heights above the ground.

A species of slow and deliberate movements, Rat Snakes frequently "freeze" in position when approached, apparently hoping to escape notice. When threatened, however, they may hiss and strike and vibrate their tails nervously.

Ratsnakes feed on small mammals and birds that they catch and constrict in coils of their body; the prey animal quickly dies of suffocation or circulatory failure before being swallowed. Ratsnakes are valuable on farms because they eat rodent pests.

In June or July, females deposit from five to 44 eggs, usually in rotted wood or in underground burrows. The young hatch in about 60 to 75 days.

Note: This snake was formerly known as the Black Ratsnake, *Elaphe obsoleta obsoleta*.

Swallowing a rodent

FOXSNAKE

Eastern

Western

46

EASTERN FOXSNAKE
(Pantherophis gloydi)

WESTERN FOXSNAKE
(Pantherophis vulpinus)

Identification:

Foxsnakes are fairly large (3 to 5 feet), yellowish to light brown snakes with black or dark brown blotches down the back and sides. The head of the adult may be reddish or orangish. The belly is yellowish with quadrangular black blotches.

At present, the two populations of the foxsnake in Michigan are considered separate species by most herpetologists (see "Distribution" below). The Eastern Foxsnake *(Pantherophis gloydi)* has fewer (average 34) but larger, darker dorsal blotches than the Western Foxsnake *(Pantherophis vulpinus)*, which has smaller, more numerous dorsal blotches (average about 41).

Distribution:

The two foxsnake species are widely separated in Michigan. The Eastern Foxsnake ranges from Saginaw Bay south along the coastal Great Lakes area to western Lake Erie. The Western Foxsnake occurs in the central and western Upper Peninsula.

Habitat and Habits:

Flat, marshy or partially drained marsh country is the habitat of the Eastern Foxsnake. The Western Foxsnake prefers open woodlands and woodland edges, fields and dune areas. The latter is locally known (Upper Peninsula) as the "pine snake", and both subspecies are often mistakenly called "copperhead" because of the reddish head coloration (see comparison photos, page 49).

Both foxsnakes are normally ground-dwelling animals that eat small mammals, birds and frogs that they kill by constriction (see description under Central Ratsnake, page 43).

When alarmed or threatened, these harmless snakes often vibrate their tails and strike repeatedly.

The Eastern Foxsnake, in particular, is declining in numbers because of habitat destruction and pollution. Both races suffer needless persecution by humans who mistakenly believe them to be venomous.

Foxsnakes lay from seven to 29 eggs in June or July, which hatch in late summer. Young specimens are similar to adults but more boldly patterned.

The Eastern Foxsnake currently is listed as THREATENED by the Michigan Department of Natural Resources (DNR) and is protected in the state. It is illegal to possess or handle this snake. Any sightings of this species should be reported to the DNR Wildlife Division in Lansing, Michigan.

Left top: head of Eastern Foxsnake; right top: head of Eastern Copperhead, a snake not found in Michigan. The Eastern Foxsnake is often called "copperhead" because of its head coloring. Note that the non-venomous foxsnake has a round eye pupil, while the venomous Copperhead has an elliptical eye pupil and a heat-sensing pit between eye and nostril.

R.D. Bartlett

Eastern Foxsnake
Found in Michigan

Eastern Copperhead
NOT found in Michigan

Juvenile

EASTERN MILKSNAKE
(Lampropeltis triangulum triangulum)

Identification:

The Eastern Milksnake is a slender, medium-sized (24 to 52 inches long) snake with brown or reddish brown, black-bordered blotches running down the light gray or tan back. There is often a Y- or V-shaped light marking on the top of the neck. The belly is white with a black checkerboard pattern. Young Eastern Milksnakes are similar to adults, but the blotches are brighter red.

Distribution:

This species occurs throughout Michigan's Lower Peninsula, and there are isolated records of its occurrence in Mackinac and Marquette counties in the Upper Peninsula.

Habitat and Habits:

These secretive snakes are found in woodlands, fields, marshes and farmlands. They often hide under boards and trash near barns and other buildings. Most often seen in spring and fall, Milksnakes appear to be primarily nocturnal in summer. The name "Milksnake" comes from the false belief that this species sucks milk from cows. They may indeed enter barns, or even houses, but in search of rodents. Because of this, they are also called barn or house snakes. Another local name sometimes given to this snake in error is "spotted adder."

In addition to rodents, Eastern Milksnakes also eat other snakes. They kill prey animals by constricting them in coils of their body. Other constricting snakes in Michigan are the Central Ratsnake and the Foxsnakes. Like many other harmless snakes, this species may vibrate its tail, hiss and strike when threatened. Many are unfortunately killed by persons who think they are venomous.

Female Eastern Milksnakes lay from six to 24 eggs in rotted wood or under debris in early summer. The brightly colored young emerge in late summer and frequently wander into garages and basements.

SMOOTH GREENSNAKE
(Opheodrys vernalis)

Identification:

The Smooth Greensnake is a small (12 to 26 inches), bright green snake with a plain whitish or yellowish belly. Occasionally, an all-brown individual may be found, but the smooth scales and lack of spots or stripes will identify this species. The newly hatched young are dark olive or gray.

Distribution:

Historically, Smooth Greensnakes have been found and recorded throughout Michigan. They remain locally common in the northern Lower Peninsula and the Upper Peninsula but are rare and found only in widely scattered locations in the southern Lower Peninsula.

Habitat and Habits:

These snakes are usually found in open, grassy places such as meadows, pastures and marsh edges. They are active, graceful little animals that rarely attempt to bite when handled, but they will emit a musky anal secretion on a captor's hand.

Greensnakes eat insects, insect larvae and spiders and can be considered beneficial to farmers and gardeners. Their diet, however, may make them particularly vulnerable to the effects of chemical pesticides.

Females lay from three to 13 tiny, cylindrical eggs in burrows or under logs or rocks. Egg laying has been recorded from June into September. Considerable embryonic development may occur prior to laying; some eggs may hatch in as few as four days, but the normal incubation period is about a month.

EASTERN MASSASAUGA RATTLESNAKE

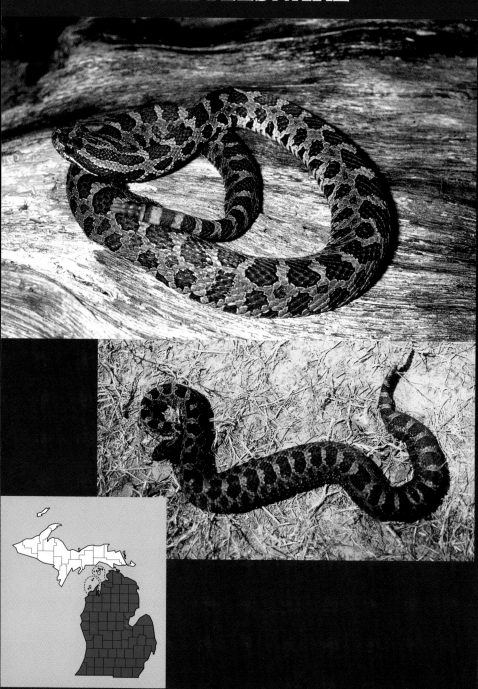

EASTERN MASSASAUGA RATTLESNAKE
(Sistrurus catenatus catenatus)

Venomous

Identification:

The Eastern Massasauga Rattlesnake is the only Michigan snake with a segmented rattle on the end of its tail. Massasaugas are medium-sized (2 to 3 feet), heavy-bodied snakes with narrow necks and an elliptical (catlike) pupil in the eye. They also have a deep facial pit on each side of the head between the eye and nostril; nerve endings in these pits can detect body heat given off by warm-blooded predators or prey.

Massasaugas are usually gray or grayish brown with dark blotches and spots down the back and sides. The belly is blackish. Young specimens are colored like the adults. **This snake is listed as a "Species of Special Concern" by the Michigan Department of Natural Resources and is a protected species in Michigan and throughout its range.**

Distribution:

The Eastern Massasauga occurs throughout the Lower Peninsula and on Bois Blanc Island, Mackinac County. There are no records for this or any other venomous snake in the Upper Peninsula.

Habitat and Habits:

The Eastern Massasauga Rattlesnake, **the only venomous snake species in Michigan**, usually inhabits wetland habitats from fall through late spring, including shrub swamps, bogs, fens and sedge marshes. In summer, they often move into upland meadows and open woodlands before returning to the lowlands for the winter. They reportedly prefer to hibernate in chimney crayfish or rodent burrows.

These shy, secretive snakes generally retreat from a disturbance and certainly do not seek confrontations with humans. They will rattle and strike if threatened, however, and will even strike without rattling if surprised.

The venom of the Massasauga is potent, but because of their relatively small size and short fangs, these animals are not considered to be as dangerous as their larger relatives found to the south and west of Michigan. Bites to humans are rare and fatalities rarer still, but the possibility of serious medical complications from a Massasauga bite does exist, especially for small children or persons already in poor health.

Exercise care when hiking in potential habitat, and leave alone any Massasaugas encountered. Too often, people have been bitten by rattlesnakes while attempting to handle or kill them. Any confirmed bite from this species should receive immediate attention at a hospital or other emergency medical care facility.

The Eastern Massasauga feeds largely on rodents, especially meadow mice, but it also eats frogs and other snakes. Diet is undoubtedly influenced by the availability of prey species in the habitat.

Female Massasaugas give birth to litters of five to 20 young in late summer. Newborn rattlesnakes have a single "button" on the tail. A new rattle segment is added at each shedding of the skin, usually several times a year, and old rattles frequently fall off. Thus the number of rattles does not correspond with the age of the snake, as is sometimes believed.

Biology of Snakes

Snake Evolution

Snakes evolved from lizards, with the earliest fossil snakes dating from the mid-Cretaceous Period (about 100 million years ago). Biologically speaking, snakes are just highly specialized lizards, but there is disagreement about which lizard lineages the snakes are most closely related to. Two prevailing ideas suggest that the immediate ancestors of snakes were either land-living burrowers or aquatic (water-dwelling). Many snake adaptations are similar to those of burrowing lizards of today, which have elongated bodies, reduced or absent limbs, and sometimes lost ear and eye structures. On the other hand, some fossil sea reptiles of the mid-Cretaceous were very snakelike but did have remnants of limbs. There are other possibilities, and additional fossil finds will be needed to clarify snake ancestry.

The most distinguishing characteristics of snakes are their lack of legs and their long, sinuous shape. Though the shape may appear uniform, it is composed of head, neck, body and tail. The neck may be conspicuous or barely distinguishable, depending on the species. The tail begins after the anal opening (vent) and may be relatively short, as in the Northern Watersnake or Eastern Milksnake, or very long, as in the Northern Ribbonsnake.

Snakes may have more than 200 bones, called vertebrae, that form the backbone and, along with the ribs, make up the entire skeleton behind the head (except in boas, pythons and other primitive snakes, which have tiny remnant hip and limb bones in their bodies). This specialized skeleton and the muscles attached to it give snakes the shape and agility that have allowed them to occupy many kinds of habitats throughout the world. Many of the internal organs of snakes are reduced in size, elongated or repositioned. For example, most species of snakes lack a fully developed left lung, the stomach is long and spindle-shaped, and the kidneys are positioned one in front of the other rather than side by side.

This elongated construction allows a snake much freedom of motion. Snakes can move forward in a straight line simply by moving the wide, flat belly scales in groups, some sliding forward, while other scales push backward against the ground. Snakes can also move forward by curving their bodies and pushing with the outside back portion of each curve. This form of movement is also used in swimming and is the way snakes move most rapidly, though they cannot move as fast as most people imagine. The top speed of the fastest Michigan snake (probably the Blue Racer) is less than 4 miles per hour, which is slower than most people can walk. Snakes have additional ways of moving, such as when climbing or moving across soft sand, but they cannot jump or arch their backs.

Another obvious feature of snakes is the forked tongue, which is a harmless sense organ. Snakes constantly extend and flick their tongues to detect odors. The tips of the tongue will pick up odor particles and transfer them to a special organ in the roof of the mouth (the Jacobson's or vomeronasal organ), which

detects the odors and then relays the information through nerves to the brain. This enhanced sense of smell is important to snakes for detecting prey and locating mates.

A third notable characteristic of snakes is that they have no eyelids. The eyes of a snake are covered by immovable, transparent layers of skin and, although a snake can move its eyes beneath this covering, it cannot blink. Several days before a snake sheds its outer skin layer, the eye coverings appear bluish and may be so clouded that the snake has very poor vision. During such times, a snake is especially shy, secretive and nervous. After the old outer skin is shed, the eye layers are completely transparent.

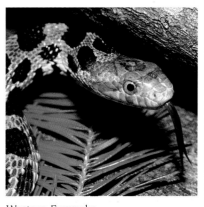

Western Foxsnake.

The lidless eyes of snakes distinguish them from legless lizards and most other reptiles. It is the unblinking eyes of snakes that probably led to the myth that snakes can hypnotize their prey. This belief may also have arisen from the fact that snakes usually remain very still before striking, waiting for their prey to move so they can confirm its location.

The Massasauga Rattlesnake can also locate its prey and potential predators by heat detection. On both sides of the front of the head, the Massasauga has heat-detecting sense organs called pits. Each pit organ is located between and slightly below the nostril and the eye.

Snakes have no external ears or ear openings, but, contrary to popular belief, snakes are not totally deaf. Snakes can detect vibrations, especially ground vibrations, through their body and jaw bones. They can also detect low frequency airborne sounds, such as those created by movement, but probably not high frequency sounds such as most birdsongs.

Other interesting features of a snake's head are the jaws, teeth and saliva. Like most of the bones in a snake's head, the jaws are only loosely connected to each other and the adjoining bones. The lower jaw consists of two halves that are joined in the front by highly flexible connective tissue, allowing them to spread wide apart. The rear ends of the lower jaws are loosely hinged to the back of the skull, allowing the snake's mouth to open very widely. Snakes eat only other animals and cannot chew their prey, so such construction is necessary to enable a snake to swallow its prey whole, especially if the animal is larger than the snake's head.

Snakes also have several rows of small, sharply pointed, backwardly curving teeth that are attached to bones that are joined loosely to the rest of the skull. Muscles move the bones and teeth back and forth to draw prey into the mouth and down the throat of the snake. Because of their small size, the teeth of non-venomous snakes are mainly used for holding and swallowing prey.

The Massasauga Rattlesnake, however, has two elongated, hollow teeth at the front of the mouth. When the snake bites, these teeth puncture the skin of the prey and conduct venom from glands in the head into the prey.

The venom is a special form of saliva that is toxic to nerve and blood tissue. The bite of a Massasauga Rattlesnake is lethal to small animals, but in most cases it would not be lethal to animals as large as a human being. Nonetheless, the bite can be dangerous because of the damage the venom can do to tissue in the vicinity of the bite, and because it may cause shock or other reactions.

Though the bite of a venomous snake such as the Massasauga can be dangerous, the bite of a non-venomous snake is usually nothing more than shallow scratches on the skin. Such bites should be promptly washed and treated with an antiseptic to prevent infection. As with any other puncture wound, you may consider seeking medical attention. Many non-venomous snakes do not attempt to bite to defend themselves but instead release a foul-smelling fluid from their anal vent or deposit body wastes on any animal attempting to pick them up. The unpleasant smell of these fluids sometimes causes the offending animal to drop the snake. No snake stings with its tail, but many snakes will vibrate their tails as a warning. Rattlesnakes make the most obvious use of this method because the dry, hardened beads of skin on the end of the tail rattle together when shaken.

It is ironic that snakes have the false reputation of being cold and slimy. The snake's skin, although covered with scales, is not covered by mucous like the scaly skin of a fish. The scales on a snake's skin are dry and the skin may feel velvety or leathery.

The skin of a snake may feel warm or cool or anywhere in between, depending on where the snake has been. Snakes are ectothermic ("cold-blooded") and cannot produce heat internally as do mammals and birds. A snake's body temperature is often nearly the same as that of the environment. Thus, a snake that has been sunning itself may feel warm when handled by a human, whereas a snake that has been swimming or lying in the shade may feel cool.

Snakes attempt to adjust their body temperature by finding a comfortable place in their habitat. A snake may sun itself to raise its body temperature so that it may better digest food or to help it become more active. Conversely, a snake may seek shade to prevent its body from overheating on a hot day. When a snake is cool or cold, it is especially vulnerable to being caught or killed by other animals.

Because snakes would freeze in the winter, they must hibernate during Michigan winters. Their hibernating places, called hibernacula, are usually underground spaces below the level of freezing soil. A suitable hibernaculum — perhaps a rodent burrow, anthill or old building foundation — may be occupied by a single snake or sometimes many snakes of the same or different species. Snakes usually come out of hibernation in April or early May in Michigan and can sometimes be seen sunning themselves around the entrance to the underground cavity.

Some snake species are especially tolerant of cold temperatures and may enter hibernation later in fall and emerge earlier in spring than less tolerant species. The Eastern Gartersnake often remains active on sunny days well into November and is often seen basking in late winter or early spring, when patches of snow are still on the ground. They are occasionally even seen in winter, swimming under the ice of ponds or streams.

Reproduction

One of the first activities that snakes engage in after coming out of hibernation is mating. As the weather warms and snakes become more active, males of some species, such as Blue Racers and Central Ratsnakes, attempt to dominate one another or chase away rivals by displays of aggression that include facing each other, raising the head and forepart of the body off the ground and pushing against each other. Female snakes release special chemicals, called pheromones, that tell the males that they are ready for mating and help the males to locate them. Mating snakes usually lie side by side or their bodies may be loosely entwined. In gartersnakes, especially, several males may simultaneously try to court a single female, sometimes forming a loose "ball" of writhing snakes.

It has recently been shown that in a few snake species, including some garter- and rattlesnakes, captive females may occasionally give birth to living young without having previously mated. To date, all of the offspring from unmated females appear to be males. It is not yet clear how often this phenomenon occurs in nature.

After mating, snakes usually spread out through the environment, seeking shelter and places where they can hide, rest, hunt and feed. During this time, they shed the old skin from the previous year. Hormone changes cause secretions in the skin to loosen the outer (epidermal) layer. The snake may rub its head and mouth against a rock, log or other object to begin the shedding process.

The snake can then slowly crawl out of the skin, leaving behind the old skin, inside-out. The skin may be shed several more times throughout the summer. Rattlesnakes add a new segment to their rattles each time they shed.

Egg-laying snakes will lay eggs during the late spring and early summer; snakes that give birth will continue to carry their developing young. The egg-laying species will usually deposit their eggs in a shallow burrow or beneath a rock or log that is warmed by the sun or in rotting vegetation where the eggs will be warmed by decomposition. The eggs hatch or the young are born during the late summer. The young soon leave the nest, or their mother, and spread out through the habitat. With the coming of fall and cold weather, all snakes begin to seek underground hibernacula and may return to the same one they used the previous year.

Snakes and People

Few people would name snakes among their favorite animals, and many people fear or at least mistrust snakes. This attitude is unfortunate because all snake species are important in the environment and most are non-venomous and harmless to humans. In fact, all the snake species in Michigan will avoid contact with humans, yet many people falsely believe that snakes will chase and attack humans or attack unprovoked from ambush. Snakes are also used as a symbol of evil, and often-repeated folklore has described impossible physical abilities to snakes, such as milking cows, hypnotizing birds, rolling in loops and stinging with their tongues or tails. People usually learn a fear of snakes in early childhood from their parents or siblings. Later in life, sensationalized print and TV stories and other fearful people reinforce this fear.

Snakes should be respected but not feared. Snakes naturally fear humans but also have instincts for self-defense, as do all wild animals. It is always best to observe and enjoy snakes in their habitats without disturbing them. Never handle a snake or any wild animal unless you know how to handle it and are prepared to accept the consequences if the animal defends itself. Never allow children to handle snakes without the assistance of a knowledgeable adult. By teaching children due caution and a respect for wild creatures, you will protect them from acquiring needless fears and protect the animals from possible injury or death.

Many snakes perform a beneficial service to humans by consuming destructive animals such as insects and rodents. All have an important place in our environment. Obviously, venomous snakes can potentially harm humans, but they need be of little concern to reasonably cautious people who understand their habits and leave them alone. There is no justification for hunting and destroying snakes of any kind in their natural habitats.

In Michigan, our only venomous snake species, the Eastern Massasauga Rattlesnake, occurs in low numbers in certain marshes, swamps and nearby uplands, and is rarely encountered by people. Further, it is a shy snake that prefers to avoid human contact. Massasaugas ocasionally wander into yards and residential areas, where their presence may be undesired — ironically, this most often occurs when recent development has usurped or disturbed their natural habitats or migration routes.

This girl is holding a Western Foxsnake, which was released after brief observation. Children should be taught to respect, not fear, snakes. Proper training in snake identification and safe handling methods is essential before attempting to pick up any snake.

Snakes and Conservation

Like many other wild animals, many kinds of snakes have declined in number because of habitat destruction and unregulated capturing and killing. Two harmless, beneficial and beautifully colored snakes, the Blue Racer and the brown and reddish yellow Eastern Foxsnake, have been nearly exterminated in southeastern Michigan. The Eastern Foxsnake is officially listed as a threatened species in Michigan. Like most other wild animals, snakes can be maintained in the environment simply by protecting or creating the habitat they require and by regulating or (when necessary) prohibiting their capture, exploitation and killing by people.

Snakes are rarely found in dense forests but prefer the edges of woods, fields and bodies of water. Dense vegetation on and near these edges will benefit snakes by providing shelter and by attracting the kinds of animals that snakes eat. Shelter includes dead trees, rotting logs, brush piles, and piles of other materials such as rock,

bark, wood chips, sawdust, etc. Tall grass growing between thickets of shrubs provides habitat for snakes and a great variety of other kinds of wildlife. Snakes also make use of artificial structures, just as other animals do. Pieces of plywood or sheet metal placed on the ground provide resting and hiding places for snakes. Snakes also require a place to hibernate, called a hibernaculum. Abandoned mammal burrows, tree root systems, and other natural cavities are the usual hibernation sites, but human-made structures are also used — snakes often enter basements and crawl spaces beneath buildings if cracks or openings are present. A snake hibernaculum can be created by filling an old building foundation, well pit, or any similar hole or depression with logs, large pieces of fieldstone, broken pieces of concrete or building blocks, and then covering the filled space with a mound of loose soil. A slanting section of ribbed plastic drain pipe extending from the bottom of the pit or excavation to the surface can allow easier snake access. Scattering additional logs and other cover objects in the vicinity of the mound will increase its attractiveness for snakes and their prey. Small mammals will soon be attracted to such easily excavated sites, and snakes may soon follow. The best locations are on well-drained, south-facing slopes.

Snakes can best be protected simply by leaving them alone, whether on your own or other private property or on public lands, and by urging others to do the same. Do not allow children to capture and hold snakes captive unless they are well supervised and well educated in snake identification, capture and care. Many snakes are inadvertently killed when improperly captured and held captive. Remember, it is illegal to capture, keep or kill reptiles that are listed as "special concern," "threatened" or "endangered" species by the Department of Natural Resources. In Michigan, shooting snakes is prohibited, and the number of snakes that can be taken from the wild is limited. For further information on laws protecting snakes, contact the Michigan Department of Natural Resources.

Central Ratsnake eating a mouse. Many snakes have habits beneficial to human interests, and all Michigan snakes play important roles in our state's natural ecology.

Snake Problems Around the Home

Most encounters with snakes in Michigan involve harmless species with habits that are often beneficial to people. If you have snakes in your yard, it is always best to learn to ignore or tolerate them, or even enjoy watching them. An inability to identify snakes is no excuse for destroying them. Michigan's one species of venomous snake is easily recognized (see Eastern Massasauga Rattlesnake, page 54). This species, and all native snakes, will generally avoid encounters with humans and escape if given the chance. However, people with true phobias regarding snakes may find it impossible to ignore their presence. In these cases, it is best to reduce the chance of encountering snakes by reducing the attractiveness of the home and yard as snake habitat.

To make your yard less attractive to snakes, eliminate any materials that would offer shelter to snakes or their prey, such as loose trash, wood, cardboard, paper and piles of lumber, firewood, bricks, pipe, sand, gravel, rocks, bark, leaves or compost. Avoid using mulch or landscape fabric or plastic, especially next to the house. Any material that would provide food for rodents and insects (snake prey) — such as pet food, wild bird seed, vegetables, fruit, garbage, etc. — should be stored in heavy plastic or metal containers with tight-fitting lids.

Snakes need cover for protection from their many enemies, so keep all grass mowed as short as possible, and trim trees and shrubs so that no foliage touches the ground. Eliminate multistemmed shrubs, and thin flowers that grow in dense clumps or continuous beds. Keep landscaping around the house and outbuildings sparse, and edge the foundation with crushed rock or pea gravel. If you follow these recommendations, you will undoubtedly see fewer snakes, though they may still occasionally venture into the yard from surrounding areas of habitat.

Snakes sometimes enter houses, garages and outbuildings in search of prey or shelter, and are perhaps most likely to enter buildings in fall, while searching for a safe place to hibernate. In Michigan, Milksnakes, Eastern Gartersnakes and Brownsnakes are the most frequent visitors, though other species may occur as well.

To Eliminate Snakes from Homes, Try These Recommendations:

1) Snakes usually enter homes through cracks or holes at or near the ground line. To deny them entry, frequently inspect and repair any openings along the foundation, especially at the ground line and at the sill plate (where the foundation meets the frame of the house), around windows and door frames, and behind or beneath porches and decks. Seal all openings 1/4 inch or wider; remember that any opening that will admit a rodent will also admit the snake that is hunting the rodent! Most snakes do not dig their own holes but simply take advantage of existing openings.

2) If rodents are present indoors, you can use traps or commercially available rodenticides. Always carefully follow label directions. It is important to note that the presence of rodents and the use of poisons to eliminate them pose a greater hazard to the people living in a home than the presence of a non-venomous snake. Further, the elimination of rodents is no guarantee that an occasional snake will not enter a house if there are still openings to the outside.

3) If a snake is found in a house and it is determined to be a non-venomous species (as most in Michigan will be), it can usually be gently scooted with a broom into an overturned deep box or flat-sided garbage can. Turn the box upright and the snake will likely be unable to scale the box or can while it is carried outdoors and released well away from the house. Smaller non-venomous snakes can be picked up directly, but wear long sleeves and gloves — any frightened animal can bite if handled. To find a snake hiding in a

basement, place several damp cloths or towels on the floor and cover with a dry cloth or piece of cardboard. The snake, in seeking moisture and a place to hide, may crawl between the cloths and can then be easily caught.

Eastern Massasauga Rattlesnakes rarely enter homes or buildings; when entry does occur, it is often associated with recent habitat destruction that has disrupted normal snake behavior.

In urban areas, there is also the possibility that a snake loose in a building is an escaped pet, possibly a non-native species. If you cannot identify a snake seen in a building or suspect that you do have a rattlesnake or other venomous species, always seek professional advice or assistance before trying to capture or destroy it.

The tiny Northern Brownsnake is often found near human dwellings in suburban and rural areas.

Preventing and Treating Snakebites

Most snakebites to humans occur when people try to tease, handle or, unfortunately, kill snakes. Few, if any, Michigan snakes will attack without being threatened in some way, and the best way to prevent snakebite is simply to leave snakes alone and unmolested. When snakebite does occur, it is important to identify the snake species involved. The great majority of bites will be from non-venomous snakes. Treating a bite from a non-venomous snake as though it were venomous will subject the victim to needless worry and expose him/her to possible complications from unneeded medical treatments.

Bites from non-venomous snakes are usually no more serious than scratches. Cleanse the wound with soap and water, treat with any commonly available antiseptic, and consider seeking professional medical advice as you would with any puncture wound. If you are uncertain whether the bite came from a venomous or a non-venomous snake, seek professional medical advice. A bite from a venomous snake will usually produce some swelling, reddening of the skin, dizziness and nausea within minutes after the bite, if venom is injected. (Note that venomous snakes do not always inject venom when they bite.)

In any case of venomous snakebite, the best advice is to get professional medical attention as fast as possible, with the least amount of physical movement by the bite victim. Do not attempt to treat a bite from a venomous snake "in the field" unless you have had specific medical training for this problem. Improper treatment could cause greater injury than the bite itself or could intensify the effect of the venom. Remember, overexcitement and exercise, such as running, can cause the venom to spread more quickly through the body. A bite from Michigan's native Massasauga Rattlesnake, while potentially serious, is almost never fatal, and most victims will experience a complete recovery. (Note: Because of the rarity of venomous snakebite in Michigan, some emergency room physicians in the state may be unfamiliar with treatment procedures. However, information should be readily available from poison control centers in the major cities.)

Eastern Massasauga Rattlesnake.

Ecology of Michigan Snakes

Aquatic fish and frog eaters
Copper-bellied Watersnake
Northern Watersnake

Aquatic crayfish eater
Queen Snake

Marsh- and field-dwelling, venomous, rodent, snake and frog eater
Eastern Massasauga Rattlesnake

Nearshore and upland foragers
Eastern Gartersnake *(opportunistic feeder)*
Northern Ribbonsnake *(mainly eats small frogs)*

Terrestrial, secretive worm eaters
Brownsnake
Butler's Gartersnake
Kirtland's Snake
Northern Red-bellied Snake
Northern Ring-necked Snake *(also eats salamanders)*

Sandy-soil-dwelling toad eater
Eastern Hog-nosed Snake

Terrestrial, meadow-dwelling insect eater
Smooth Greensnake

Terrestrial, rodent-eating constrictors
Central Ratsnake
Eastern Foxsnake *(marsh-dwelling)*
Eastern Milksnake
Western Foxsnake

Terrestrial, fast-moving frog, reptile and rodent eater
Blue Racer

For More Information

Behler, J.L. 1999. *National Audubon Society First Field Guide: Reptiles.* New York: Scholastic, Inc.

Cogger, H.G., and R.G. Zweifel (eds.). 1998. *Encyclopedia of Reptiles and Amphibians* (2nd ed.) San Diego: Academic Press.

Conant, R., and J.T. Collins. 1998. *A Field Guide to Reptiles and Amphibians of Eastern and Central North America* (3rd ed., expanded). Boston: Houghton Mifflin Co.

Crother, B. (committee chair) et al. 2000. *Scientific and Standard English Names of Amphibians and Reptiles of North America North of Mexico, with Comments Regarding Confidence in Our Understanding.* Herp. Circ. No. 29. Society for the Study of Amphibians and Reptiles. (For updates, see the SSAR Web site: http://www.ssarherps.org/.)

Ernst, C.H., and E.M. Ernst. 2003. *Snakes of the United States and Canada.* Washington, D.C.: Smithsonian Books.

Ernst, C.H., and G.R. Zug. 1996. *Snakes in Question.* Washington, D.C.: Smithsonian Institution Press.

Greene, H.W. 1997. *Snakes: The Evolution of Mystery in Nature.* Berkeley: University of California Press.

Harding, J.H. 1997. *Amphibians and Reptiles of the Great Lakes Region.* Ann Arbor: University of Michigan Press.

R.W. VanDevender

Kirtland's Snake.

74